The Corrs

Wise Publications
London/New York/Paris/Sydney/Copenhagen/Madrid/Tokyo

Exclusive Distributors:
Music Sales Limited
8/9 Frith Street, London W1D 3JB, England.
Music Sales Pty Limited
120 Rothschild Avenue, Rosebery, NSW 2018, Australia.

Order No. AM968110
ISBN 0-7119-8573-1
This book © Copyright 2000 by Wise Publications

Compiled and arranged by Stephen Duro
Music processed by Allegro Reproductions
Cover photograph courtesy of Rex Features

Printed in the United Kingdom by
Printwise (Haverhill) Limited, Suffolk

Your Guarantee of Quality
As publishers, we strive to produce every book to the highest commercial standards.
The music has been freshly engraved and the book has been carefully designed to minimise awkward page turns and to make playing from it a real pleasure.
Particular care has been given to specifying acid-free, neutral-sized paper made from pulps which have not been elemental chlorine bleached. This pulp is from farmed sustainable forests and was produced with special regard for the environment.
Throughout, the printing and binding have been planned to ensure a sturdy, attractive publication which should give years of enjoyment.
If your copy fails to meet our high standards, please inform us and we will gladly replace it.

Music Sales' complete catalogue describes thousands of titles and is available in full colour sections by subject, direct from Music Sales Limited. Please state your areas of interest and send a cheque/postal order for £1.50 for postage to:
Music Sales Limited, Newmarket Road, Bury St. Edmunds, Suffolk IP33 3YB.

www.musicsales.com

At Your Side

Words & Music by Andrea Corr, Caroline Corr, Sharon Corr & Jim Corr

Moderately

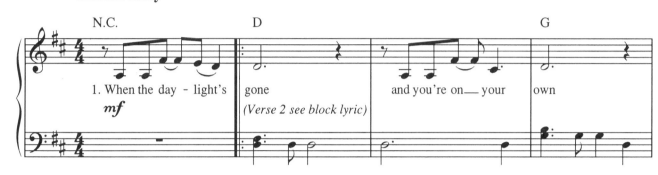

1. When the day - light's gone *(Verse 2 see block lyric)* and you're on__ your own *mf*

and you need a__ friend__ just to be a - round,

I will com - fort you, I will take your__ hand__ and I'll pull you__

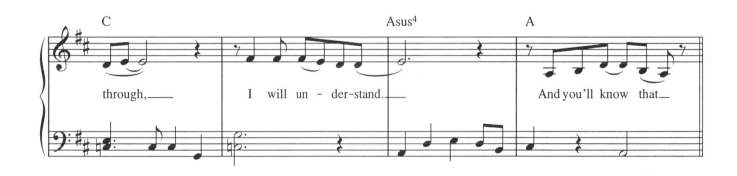

through,__ I will un - der - stand.__ And you'll know that__

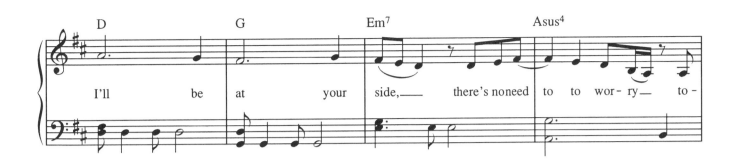

D   G   Em⁷   Asus⁴

I'll   be   at   your   side,___   there's noneed   to   to   wor - ry___   to-

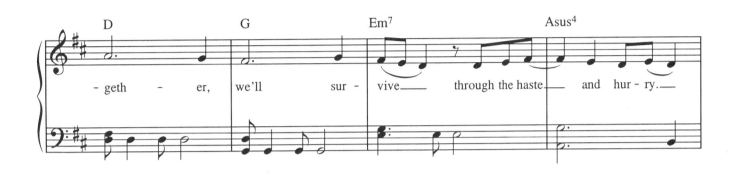

D   G   Em⁷   Asus⁴

- geth - er,   we'll   sur - vive___   through the haste___   and   hur - ry.___

D   G   Em⁷   Asus⁴

I'll   be   at___   your   side,___   when you feel___   like you're a - lone___

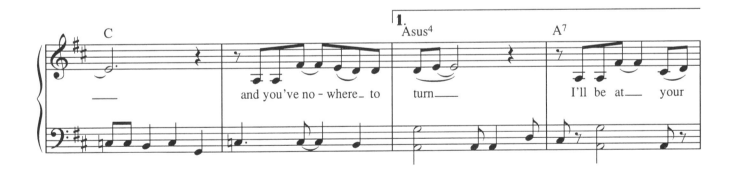

C   **1.** Asus⁴   A⁷

and you've no - where___ to   turn___   I'll be at___   your

D   G   Em   Asus⁴

side.   2. If   life's   stand - ing___

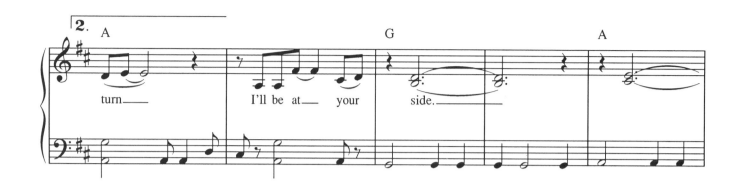

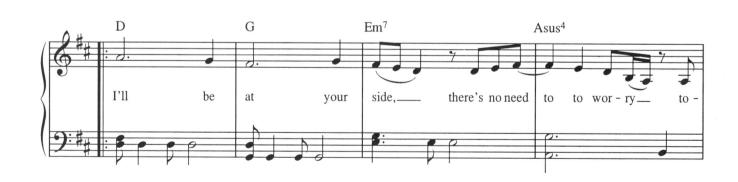

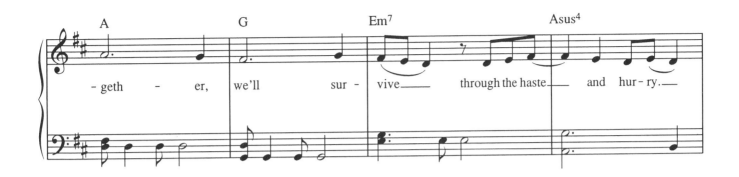

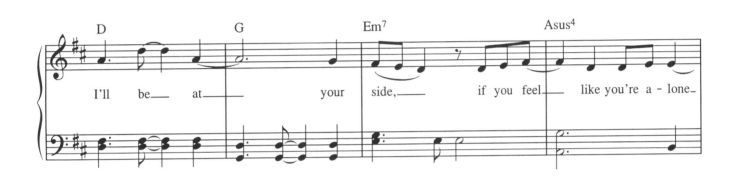

Verse 2:

If life's standing still and your soul's confused
And you cannot find what road to choose
If you make mistakes you won't let me down
I will still believe I won't turn around.

And you know that *etc*

Breathless

Words & Music by R.J. Lange, Andrea Corr,
Caroline Corr, Sharon Corr & Jim Corr

Moderately

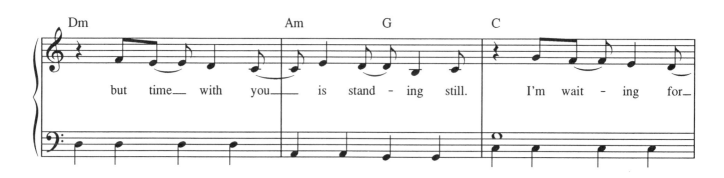

Tempt__ me,   tease__ me__   un - til I   can't de - ny__ this

lov - ing__ feel - ing.__   Make me   long for your__ kiss.__

Go__ on,   go__ on,__   Yeah,__   come on.__

__ come on.__   go__ on,   go__ on,__   come on,

leave me breath - less.___ go___ on, go___ on,___ come on,

leave me breath - less.___ go___ on, go___ on,___ come on,

leave me breath - less.___ go___ on, go___ on.

Verse 2:

And if there's no tomorrow
And all we have is here and now
I'm happy just to have you
You're all the love I need somehow
It's like a dream
Although I'm not asleep
And I never want to wake up
Don't lose it, don't leave it.

So go on, go on *etc.*

Dreams

Words & Music by Stevie Nicks

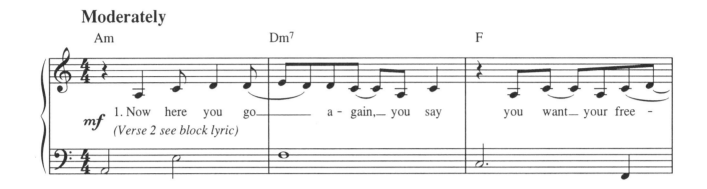

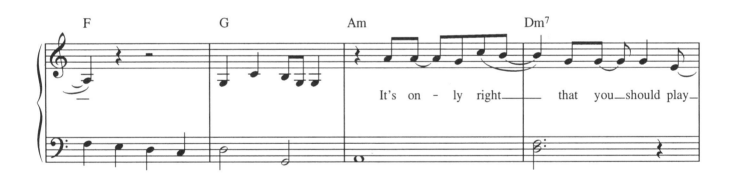

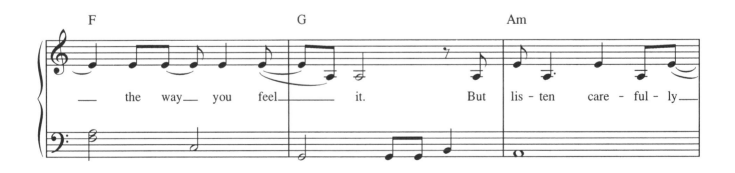

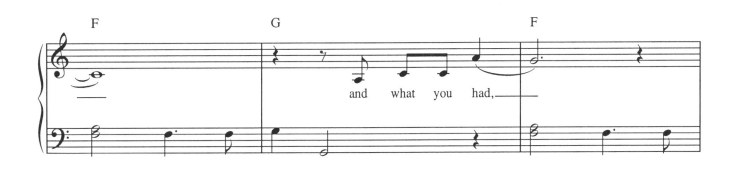

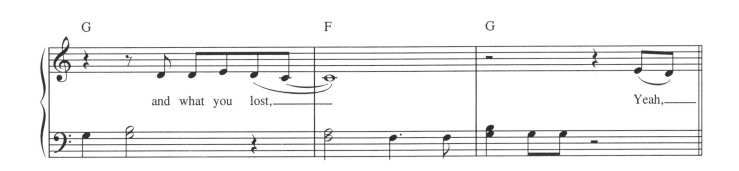

thun - der on - ly hap - pens when it's rain - ing.

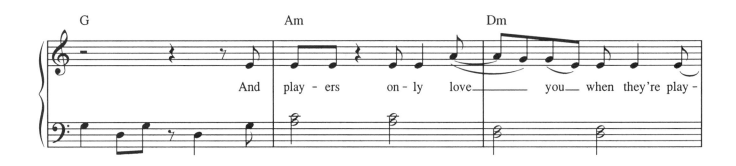

And play - ers on - ly love you when they're play -

- ing. Yeah, wo - men they will come

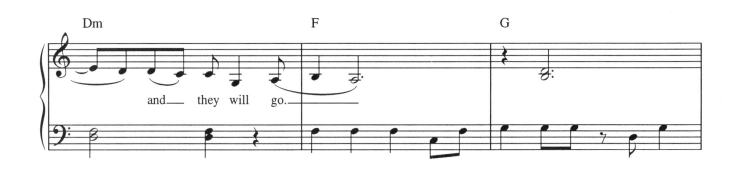

and they will go.

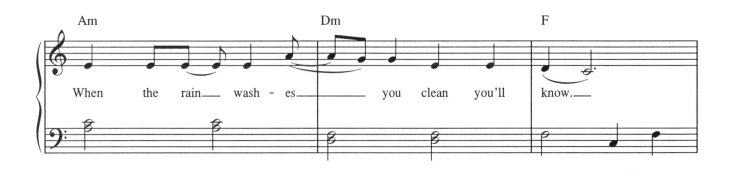

When the rain wash - es you clean you'll know.

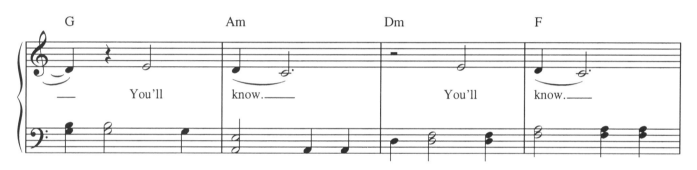

Verse 2:

Now here I go again I see the crystal vision
But I keep my visions to myself
Well it's only me who wants to wrap around your dreams
And have you any dreams you'd like to sell?
Dreams of loneliness.

Like a heartbeat *etc*.

15

Forgiven, Not Forgotten

Words & Music by Andrea Corr, Caroline Corr, Sharon Corr & Jim Corr

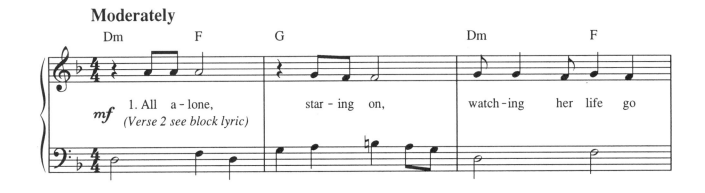

1. All a-lone, *(Verse 2 see block lyric)* star - ing on, watch-ing her life go

by. When her days are— grey and her nights— are black,

dif-f'rent shades of mun - dane, And the one-eyed fur - ry toy that

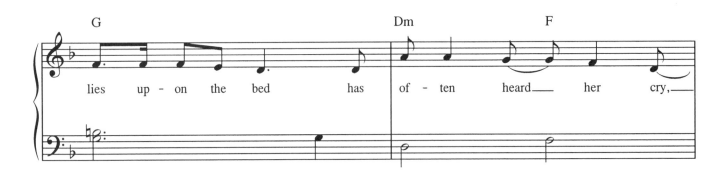

lies up - on the bed has of - ten heard— her cry,

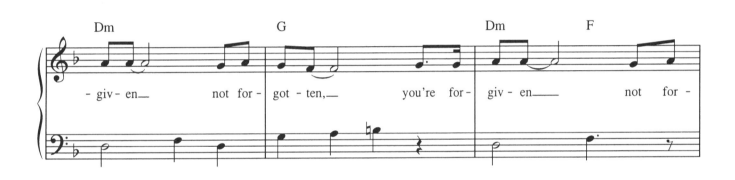

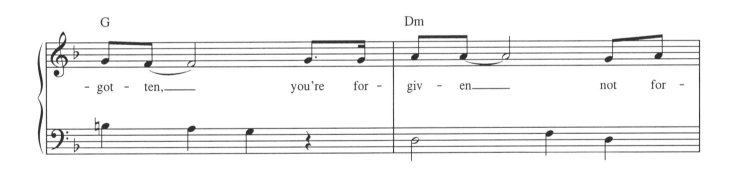

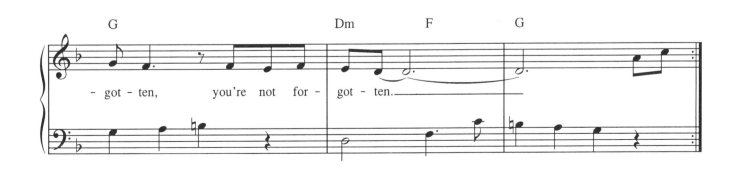

Still a - lone,_____ star - ing on,

wish - ing her life good - bye.____ As she goes search - ing for a man long for - giv -

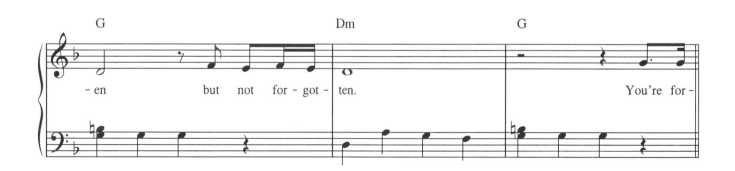

- en but not for - got - ten. You're for -

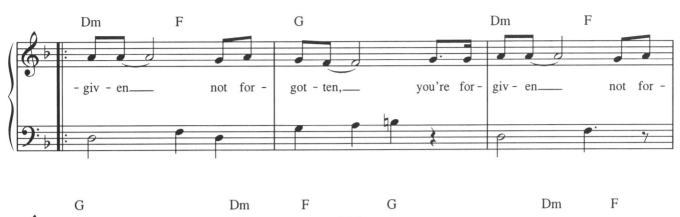

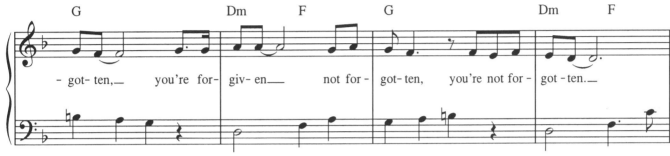

Verse 2:

A bleeding heart torn apart
Left on an icy grave
And a room where they once lay
Face to face
Nothing could get in their way
But now the memories of the man
Are haunting her days
And the craving never fades
She's still dreaming of a man.
Long forgiven
But not forgotten.

You're forgiven *etc.*

Love To Love You

Words & Music by Andrea Corr, Caroline Corr, Sharon Corr & Jim Corr

Moderately

I would love to love you like you do me.

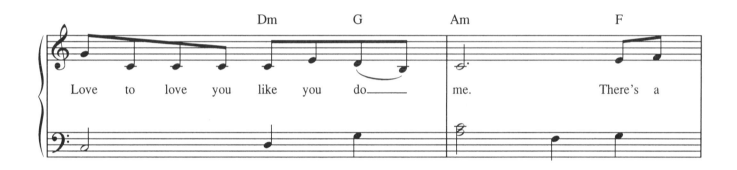

Love to love you like you do me. There's a

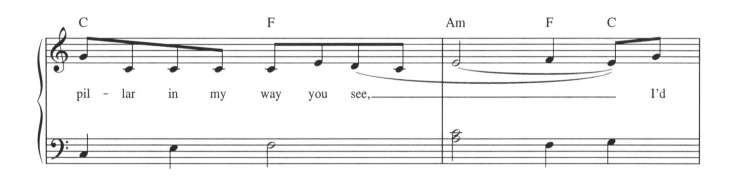

pil - lar in my way you see, I'd

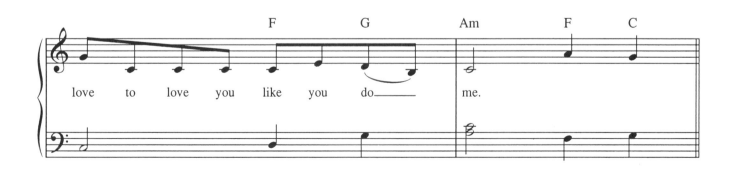

love to love you like you do me.

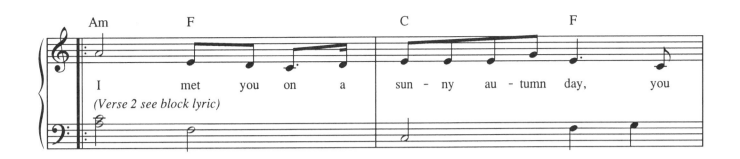

Am   F   C   F

I   met   you   on   a   sun - ny   au - tumn   day,   you

(Verse 2 see block lyric)

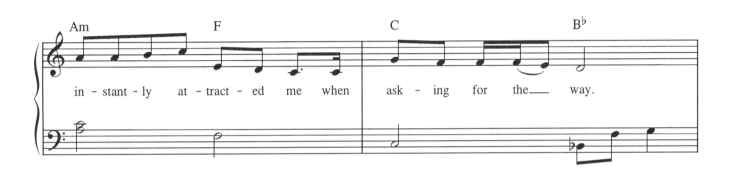

Am   F   C   B♭

in - stant - ly   at - tract - ed   me   when   ask - ing   for   the___ way.

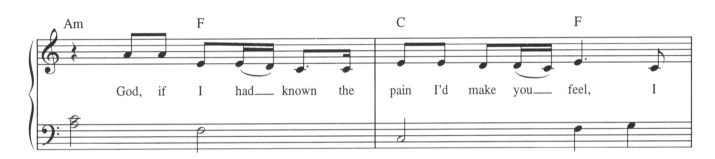

Am   F   C   F

God,   if   I   had___ known   the   pain   I'd   make   you___ feel,   I

Am   F   C   B♭

would   have   stopped   this   thought   of   us   and   turned   up - on   my   heel.___

G   C   F   C   G

Though   you   should   leave   me,   time   make   it   be   al - right.

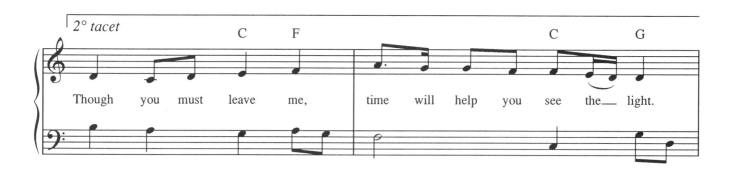

2° tacet

C   F   C   G

Though you must leave me,   time will help you see the— light.

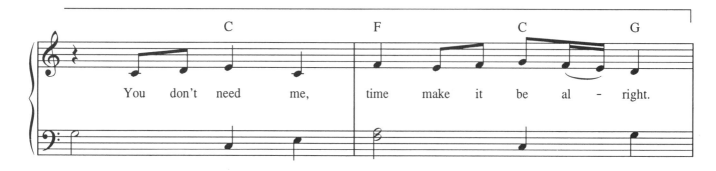

C   F   C   G

You don't need me,   time make it be al – right.

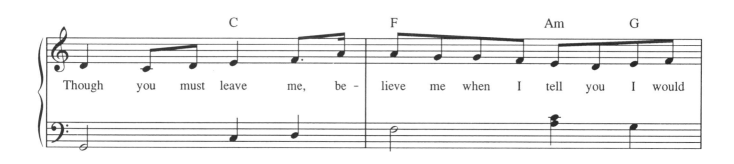

C   F   Am   G

Though you must leave me, be - lieve me when I tell you I would

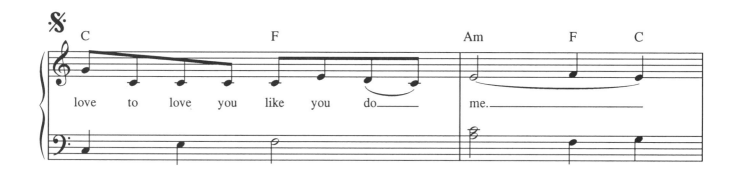

C   F   Am   F   C

love to love you like you do— me.—

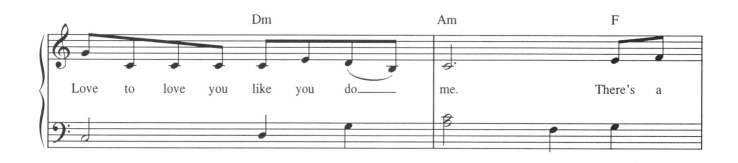

Dm   Am   F

Love to love you like you do— me.   There's a

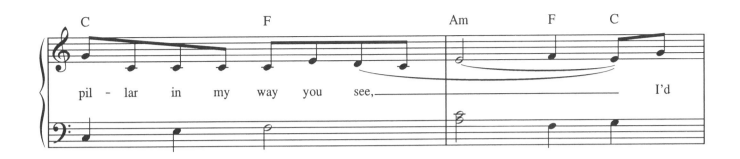

pil - lar in my way you see,_____ I'd

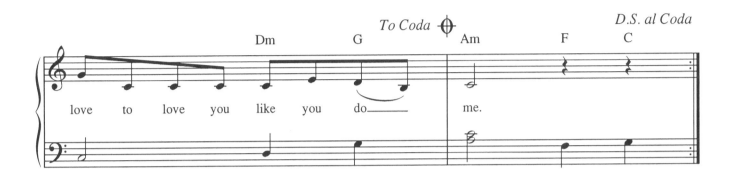

love to love you like you do_____ me.

To Coda ⊕ *D.S. al Coda*

⊕ *CODA*

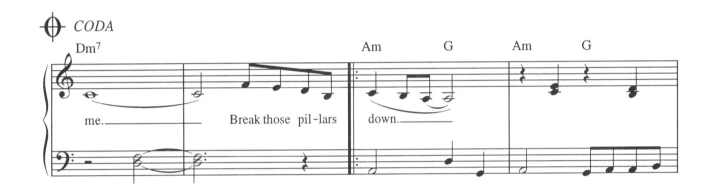

me._____ Break those pil-lars down._____

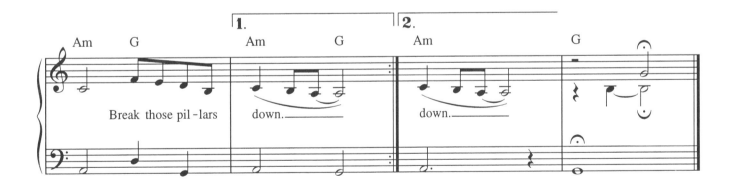

Break those pil-lars down._____ down._____

1. **2.**

Verse 2:

You recognised my barrier to love
I know there's nothing worse than unrequited love.
I prayed to God that I could give the love you gave to me
But something's lying in my way
Preventing it to be.

No More Cry

Words & Music by Andrea Corr, Caroline Corr, Sharon Corr & Jim Corr

Moderately

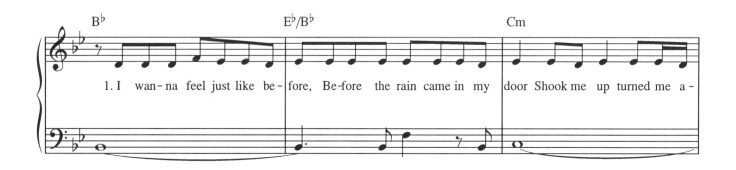

1. I wan-na feel just like be-fore, Be-fore the rain came in my door Shook me up turned me a-

-round Made me cry till I would drown Stole the day-light, brought the night So much an-ger I would

fight Lost my youth a-mid the blue Saw all the lone-li-ness in you. 2. Wan-na help you, give you

(Verse 3 see block lyric)

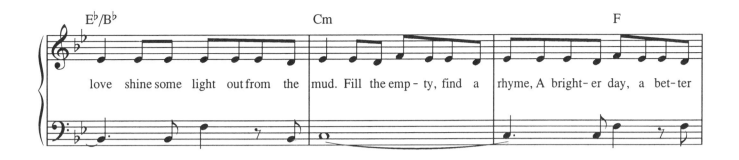

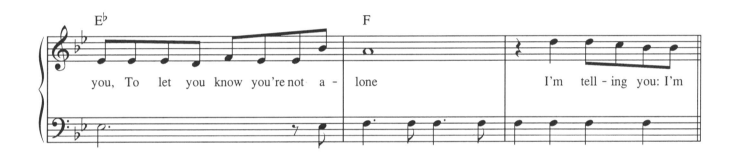

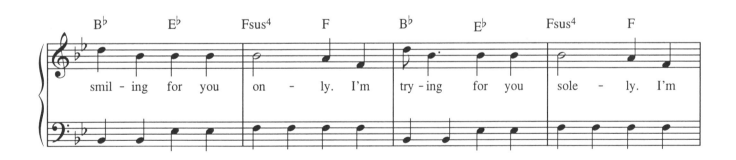

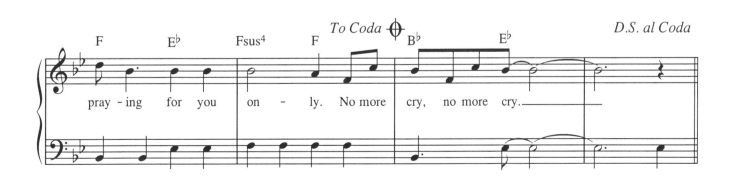

cry, no more cry._____ I'm sing - ing for you

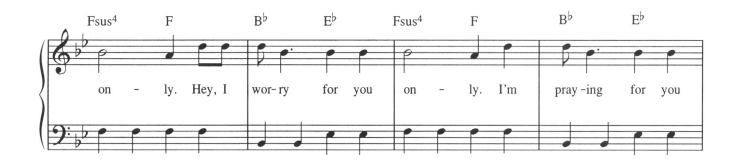

on - ly. Hey, I wor-ry for you on - ly. I'm pray -ing for you

on - ly. No more cry, no more cry._____

Reach out for your love.___ Shout out for your love.___

Lis - ten for your love.___ Be -lieve in her love.___

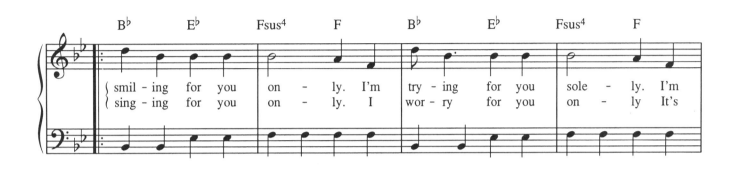

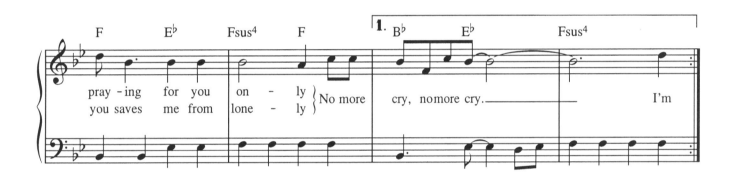

Verse 3:

I wanna hear you laugh again
Without the ache to bring you down
No we'll never be the same
If only I could take your pain
But if it's true what people say
There still is beauty in each day
We'll find comfort in her strength
And one day soon we'll meet again ...
I'm telling you:
I'm smiling for you *etc.*

Only When I Sleep

Words & Music by Andrea Corr, Caroline Corr, Sharon Corr,
Jim Corr, John Shanks, Paul Peterson & Oliver Leiber

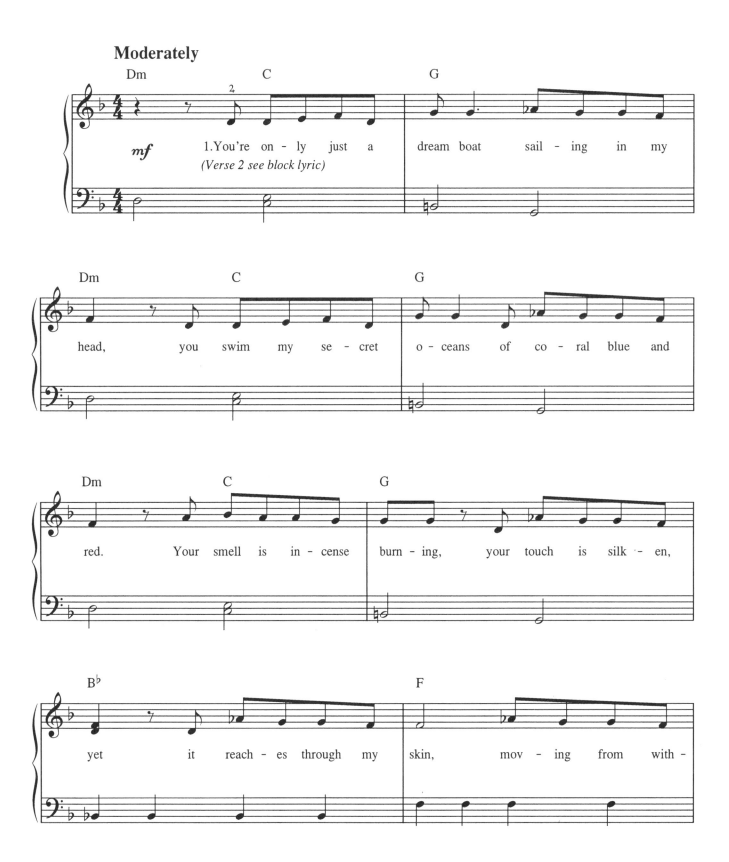

-in, and clutch-es at my breast. But it's on-ly when I sleep, see you in my

dreams, got me spin-ning round and round turn-ing up-side down. I hear you
But I on-ly

breathe some-where in my sleep, got me spin-ning round and round turn-ing

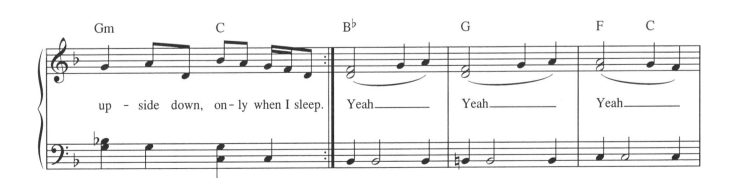

up - side down, on-ly when I sleep. Yeah Yeah Yeah

But it's on-ly when I sleep.____

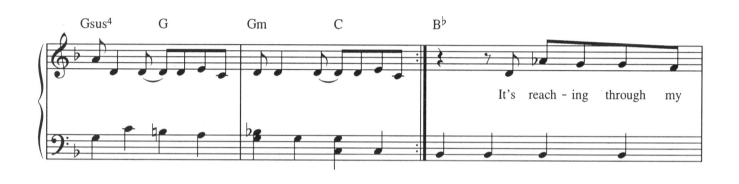

It's reach-ing through my

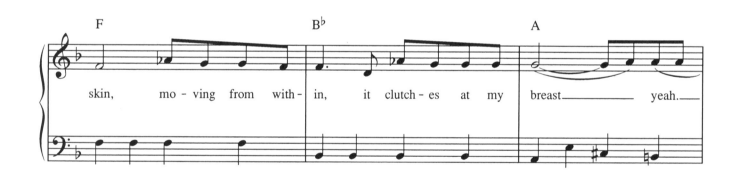

skin, mo-ving from with-in, it clutch-es at my breast_____ yeah.____

____ But it's on-ly when I sleep,____ See you in my dreams, got me spin-ning

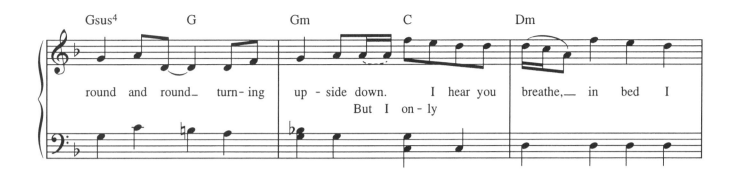

round and round— turn-ing | up - side down. I hear you | breathe,— in bed I
But I on - ly

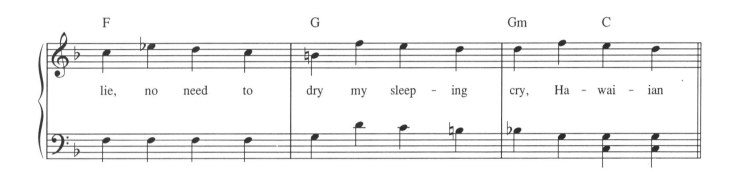

lie, no need to | dry my sleep — ing | cry, Ha - wai - ian

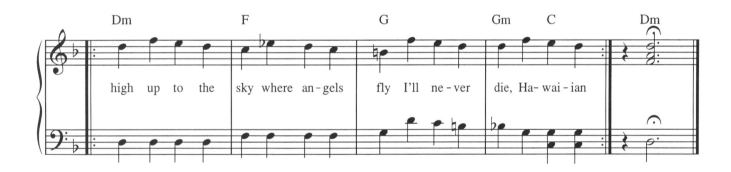

high up to the | sky where an-gels | fly I'll ne - ver | die, Ha-wai-ian

Verse 2:

And when I wake from slumber
Your shadow's disappeared
Your breath is just a sea mist
Surrounding my body
I'm working through the daytime
But when it's time to rest
I'm lying in my bed
Listening to my breath
Falling from the edge
But I only hear you breathe *etc.*

Runaway

Words & Music by Andrea Corr, Caroline Corr, Sharon Corr & Jim Corr

Moderately

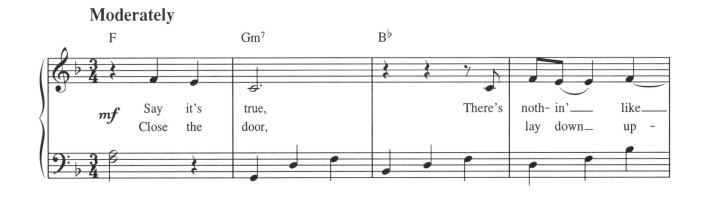

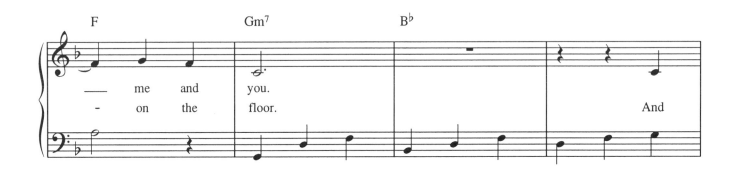

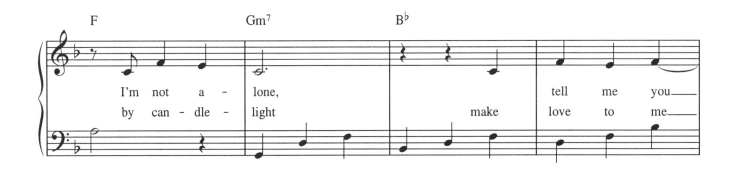

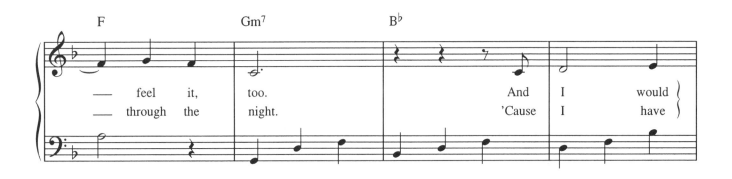

you.

D.S. al Coda

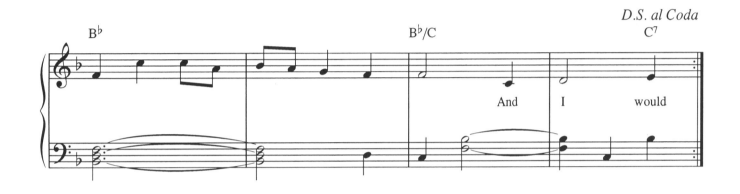

And   I   would

CODA

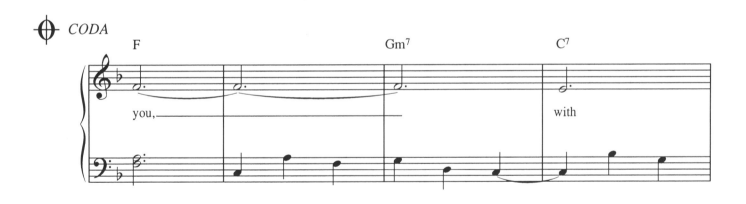

you,_____   with

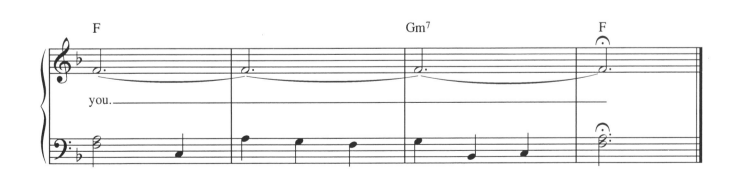

you._____

35

So Young

Words & Music by Andrea Corr, Caroline Corr, Sharon Corr & Jim Corr

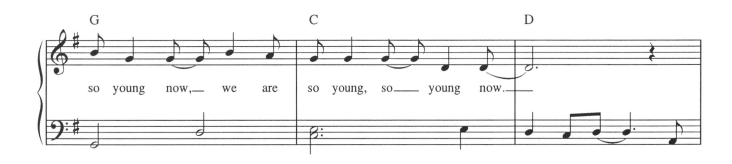

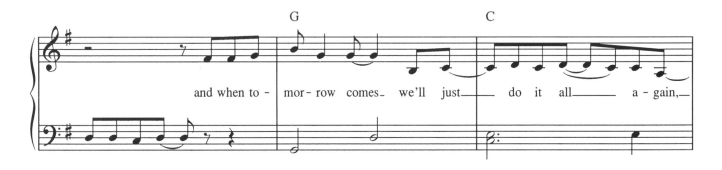

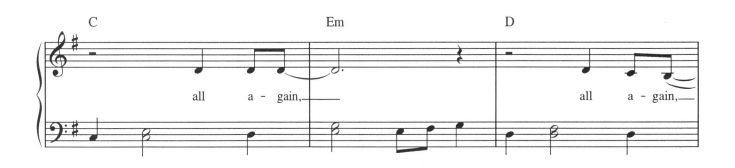

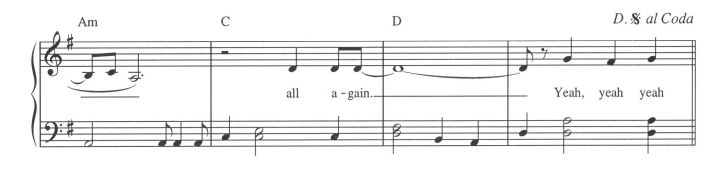

all a-gain. Yeah, yeah yeah

CODA

We are so

Yeah yeah yeah yeah yeah.
young,

yeah.

We are so

Yeah yeah
young,

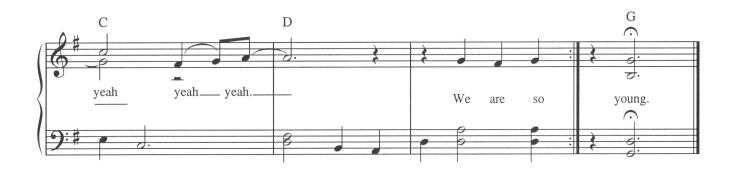

yeah yeah yeah.

We are so young.

Verse 2:

And we are chasing the moon
Just running wild and free,
We are following through
Every dream and every need.

'Cause we are so young now *etc.*

What Can I Do

Words & Music by Andrea Corr, Caroline Corr, Sharon Corr & Jim Corr

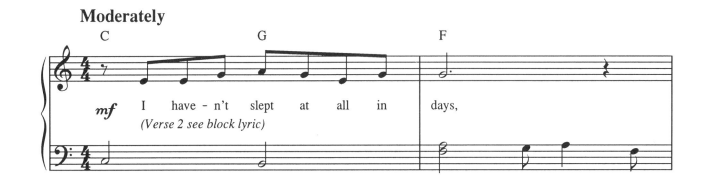

I have - n't slept at all in days, *(Verse 2 see block lyric)*

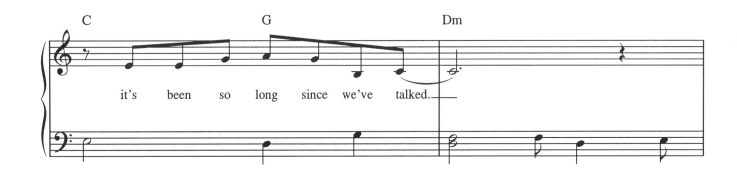

it's been so long since we've talked.

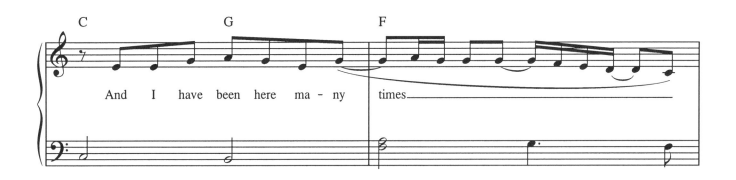

And I have been here ma - ny times

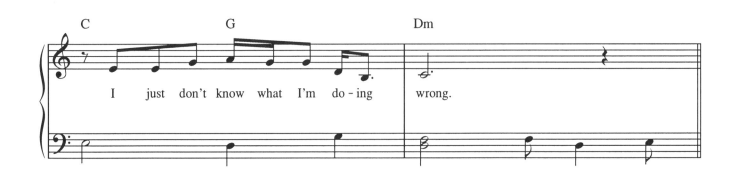

I just don't know what I'm do - ing wrong.

41

Love me, love me, love love me,

love me, love, love me, love me, love,

love me, love me, love, love me.

Verse 2:

There's only so much I can take
And I just got to let it go
And who knows I might feel better
If I don't try and I don't hope.

What can I do *etc.*

Radio

Words & Music by Andrea Corr, Caroline Corr, Sharon Corr & Jim Corr

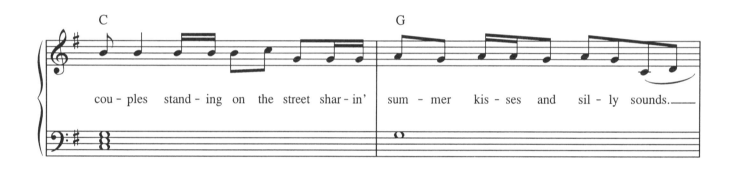

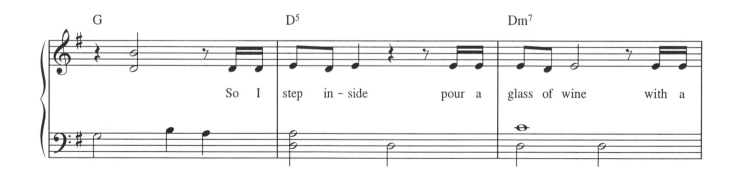

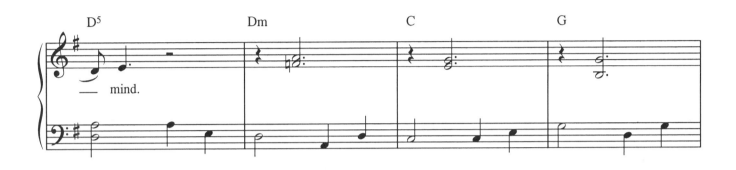

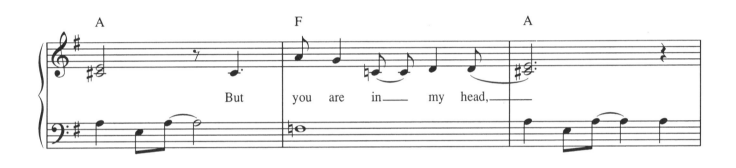

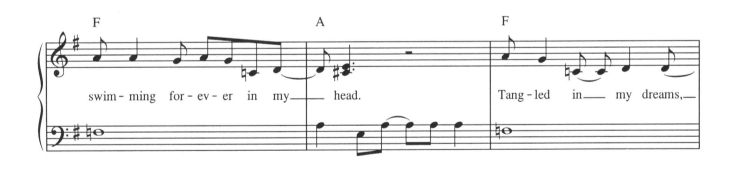

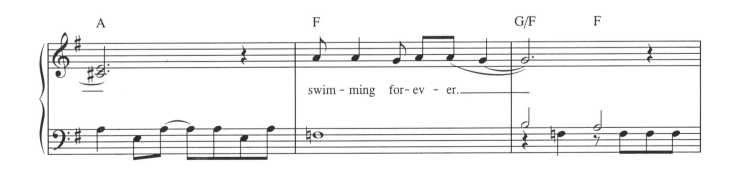

So I list- ten to the ra - di - o,___ and all the songs we used to know,___

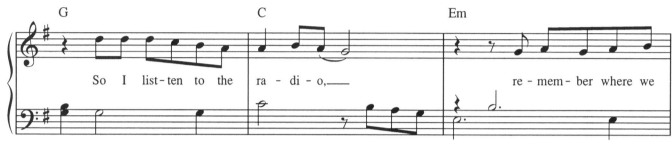

So I list-ten to the ra - di - o,___ re - mem - ber where we

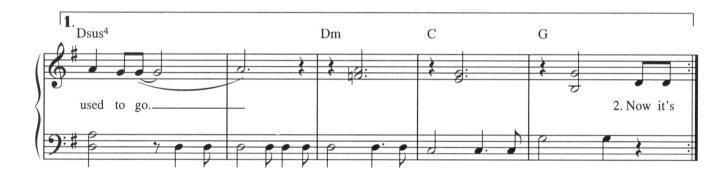

used to go.___ 2. Now it's

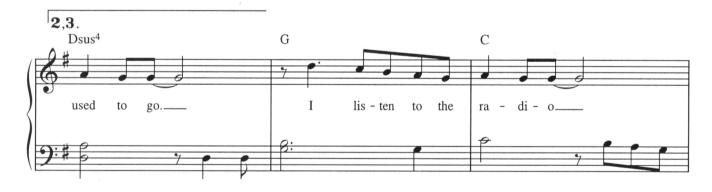

used to go.___ I lis - ten to the ra - di - o___

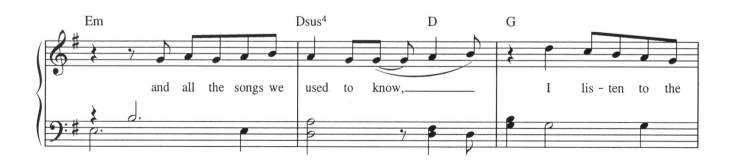

and all the songs we used to know,___ I lis - ten to the

46

head.

Tang-led in my dreams,

D.S. al Coda

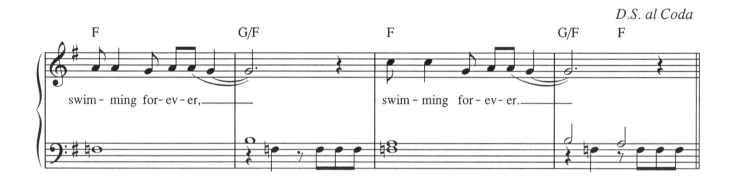

swim-ming for-ev-er,

swim-ming for-ev-er.

CODA

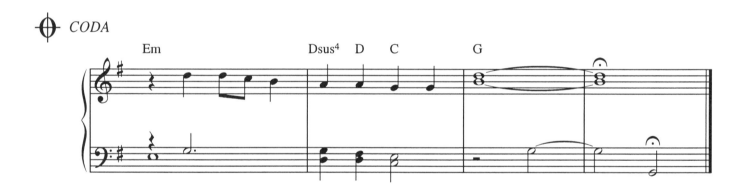

Verse 2:

Now it's morning light and it's cold outside
Caught up in a distant dream
I turn and think that you are by my side
So I leave my bed and I try to dress
Wondering why my mind plays tricks
And fools me in to thinking you are there
But you're just in my head
Swimming forever in my head
Not lying in my bed
Just swimming forever.

So listen to the radio *etc.*